About the Author

Laura de Bono lives in Tonbridge, Kent, with her husband and three children. Her life changed dramatically in 2013, aged forty-seven, when she experienced a devastating post-operation cerebral vasospasm, leading to brain damage and disability. This is her first book.

Losing My Mind

Insider Knowledge to Understand Dementia

Laura de Bono

Losing My Mind

Insider Knowledge to Understand Dementia

Olympia Publishers
London

www.olympiapublishers.com
OLYMPIA PAPERBACK EDITION

A CIP catalogue record for this title is
available from the British Library.

ISBN: 978-1-78830-912-7

First Published in 2021

Olympia Publishers
Tallis House
2 Tallis Street
London
EC4Y 0AB

Printed in Great Britain

Dedication

For my heroic husband, Caspar, and my understanding and supporting children, Max, Joe, and Rose.

Author's Note

This humorous book is laughing at myself, not laughing at dementia – it's no laughing matter. I use humour to cope with my situation because I can see a light through this long, dark tunnel. My brain is recovering with new growth of brain cell connections. Dementia is quite the opposite – dementia is for always. So please don't ignore it, but try to understand it and act on your new found empathy.

Chapter One
An Introduction to Dementia

The common phrase "I'm losing my mind" is, for some of us, only playful semantics for forgetful behaviour. Forgetfulness is a common trait of busy lives, but it isn't a sign of brain cell deficiency. In fact, it's only distractions intervening to break the line of thought.

The phrase is true in dementia.

The word comes from Latin: "de" is "from" and the Latin word for mind is "mens". Hence "dementia" is a condition of people who "lost their minds".

Dementia is an ever-increasing condition due to our greater awareness and the increasingly older population in the West.

Dementia is not a disease, but a general term to describe the symptoms of loss of memory, communication and thinking.

It is caused by damage to the brain cells, therefore an inability to communicate with each other.

Types of Dementia

Doctors differentiate types of dementias from the causes:

Alzheimer's is by protein abnormalities growing plaques or "tangles" within cells. This is the most common.

Dementia with Lewy bodies is linked to abnormal brain structure, resulting from cell death caused by oxygen deprivation of the brain cells.

Vascular dementia results from cell death caused by oxygen deprivation of the brain cells as in a stroke (blood clots) or a bleed which interrupts or reduces blood supply. I had similar cell death.

Symptoms of Dementia

There are several symptoms of dementia:

Short-term memory loss. For example, asking the same question repeatedly in a short space of time.

Long-term memory loss. For example, not recognising family members or close friends.

Difficulty completing familiar tasks. For example, dressing themselves.

Communication problems. For example, forgetting simple words or using the wrong ones.

Disorientation. For example, getting lost on a previously familiar street or forgetting their home's room layout.

Problems with abstract thinking. For example, dealing with money or telling the time.

Misplacing objects. For example, forgetting the location of everyday items such as keys, wallets or glasses.

Mood Changes. For example, sudden and unexplained changes in outlook.

Personality changes. For example, becoming suddenly suspicious, irritable or fearful.

Loss of initiative. For example, showing less interest in starting something or going somewhere.

As the sufferer ages, these symptoms tend to worsen.

Chapter Two
My Story

My brain damage is similar to dementia but, thankfully, it's recovering with new growth of brain cell connections. It's a slow and tough recovery, but it's there.

In May 2013 an innocuous visit to the opticians, which spied a suspicious field test, resulted in discovering a massive 4cm temporal epidermoid cyst touching my right optic nerve. It's a type of brain tumour and started slowly growing at birth. I discovered it aged 47, married with three dependent children, aged 8, 11 and 12.

I feared the worst. My imagination went into overload – I imagined the cyst enveloping my brain like a parasite, smothering my brain. I thought my contented and fulfilled life was ended. I had three small jobs at a local public school and together with many interests, I ran the home while my husband was busy at work. The children were in the difficult period of transferring to secondary school. They needed me.

My fears of the growing cyst (albeit very slowly) totally consumed me, and I wanted to get rid of it immediately. The neurosurgeon at the highly rated King's College Hospital, SE London, assured me the removal of the cyst, despite its size, is a simple procedure and many people had it done successfully. When the first available appointment came up, I took it, despite it being on our 15th wedding anniversary. We will celebrate it the day after with my coming home.

We didn't celebrate it that year.

It went wrong after the surgery when a severe vasospasm occurred. An increase of pressure in my brain deprived some of the brain of oxygen, thus brain damage. It resulted in hemi-paresis (half of my body was paralysed) and my speech and language was gone - I couldn't move my left side and couldn't communicate at all. The surgeon saved my life by doing a decompressive craniectomy – slicing off the top of my skull – to relieve the pressure in my brain.

I woke up to a living nightmare – I awoke in the alien Intensive Care speechless, wordless, paralysed, and choking on some liquid pouring into my mouth. I thought it was blood and spat it out…it was a drip they inserted through my nose and the liquid was life-saving nutrients. Whoops!

No explanation, no kind words. I was alone, confused and frightened. I suddenly heard a woman's shout close by me, "This one doesn't speak."

That was my introduction to hospital care.

Three long months in three hospitals was like a hostage situation.

I was imprisoned in my useless body, surrounded by strange sights and sounds. My left side didn't work; therefore, I couldn't even sit up, let alone walk. Plus, I couldn't speak – I couldn't ask for help if any staff came my way. I needed help twenty-four hours a day from the unmotivated nurses, busy support carers and therapists, and distant doctors. Some were wonderfully empathic and caring, some were not. When I was moved nearer home, my family and friends also helped.

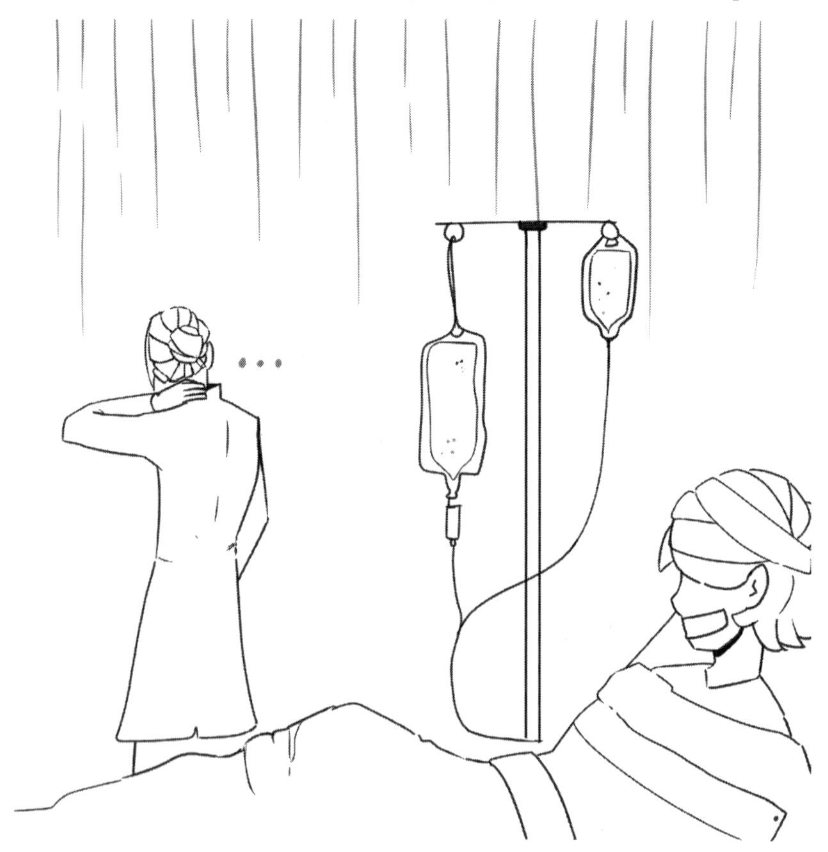

I returned home in a wheelchair (which I couldn't push myself with one hand) and semi-silent with dysarthria (difficulties of speech formation) and expressive aphasia (confusion over the correct words and the sentence order), but relieved to be home.

My husband and children survived the crisis by courage, initiative, and lots of support from friends and family.

My recovery at home began straight away. The NHS Community Therapy Team were struggling with a massive workload and a staff crisis and so we hired a neuro-physio and a language therapist. Also, I needed a live-in carer to wash me, dress me and make my meals. It hit me at home my previous life had gone. I was transformed from an independent, healthy and fit, busy woman to a frustrated, dependent, disabled, non-communicative shadow of myself.

And I had to mentally learn life again under unrealistic expectant friends' and family's scrutiny. My positive thinking (some people would say delusional thinking!), determination, and hard work were the greatest drivers to recovery, but underlying realisations came slowly and surely.

I withdrew into my home, only engaging with knowledgeable therapists and my immediate family who understood my challenges. People sympathised with the obvious physical disabilities, but the hidden one – fatigue (the medical word for extreme tiredness) – was my invisible conquering enemy. My recovering brain had to work very hard because it needed to work all the time to acquire and remember new skills. I needed to learn and think to balance, walk and talk. These functions we learn long ago in childhood and don't think about them at all. They just exist in our subconscious. Added to that, I needed to learn to function in modern day life – to use the kitchen gadgets again, including the oven, the kettle, and the washing machine and to relearn to dress and wash myself with only one hand.

I have difficulty measuring time – our baked potatoes were black wrinkled hard stones when I estimated ten hours to cook! Added to that, I have difficulty thinking holistically. With a carefully prepared one-tray family meal, I remembered to turn the timer alarm off, but didn't stop cooking it!

It was easier to work out my laptop and mobile – no sheet of instructions with tiny print in an array of languages…just common sense, one-step icons to follow.

Thus, my brain has to work constantly, learning about new circumstances, especially multitasking when I need to speak.

Fatigue is like your brain shutting down. Think of bad flu, jet lag, and a hangover mixed together at the same time and needing to speak in a foreign language. It's difficult to function. You want to crawl into bed and to be alone. I overcome it by lots of day-sleeps on my reclining chair and long nights in bed. Like a baby, my brain needs lots of rest.

It's slowly getting better, but it's always there and limits me every day. In seven years, I haven't spent a whole day away from my home or temporary bed. Out of necessity, I sleep upright on a chair in a noisy café to rest my tired-out brain to people's bemusement.

I try to rest my brain by listening to music and audio books instead of sleeping by lessening my reliance on sleep. Recent technology is a life saver – my smart phone and my laptop are constant companions and I have "read" a variety of audio books including the greats and non-fiction you never find time to read– my recovering brain is thirsty for new knowledge and understanding.

The seizures started in the second year at home. It's very frightening. Muscles take over the body as a tidal wave of instructions from the brain commands them, like an opened dam sending a gigantic wave of water downstream. I couldn't correct my body to control it. The result was falling onto the ground with a crash on my head – I couldn't soften my fall with my arm or hand.

Luckily, the titanium plate did its purpose to protect my brain. I underwent a reconstructive cranioplasty in January 2014. A custom-made titanium plate was stapled on my skull under my scalp to replace the missing piece of skull. The third general anaesthetic in two years.

I was awake when the doctor removed the staples with a pair of pliers. Removing stitches from flesh is a walk in the park compared with staples from the skull!

Eventually, we (my GP, my neurologist and I) found the right combination of anti-seizure medicines to get them under control. Thankfully, they are now controlled with taking meds each morning and evening.

My right optic nerve hasn't recovered; therefore, I haven't the left field of vision. I can see normally because my recovering brain has adapted to my sight. But the DVLA refuses to listen to me because I failed their linear, one-size-fits-all test for field vision. I am banned from driving despite pleas of my limited mobility. The Department of Work and Pensions thinks I need to drive… it awards me a blue badge every year. Do these government bodies communicate with each other?!

After seven years of intense neuro-physio and hard work, my home life is now independent – I can do my personal care myself and look after the home (except the ironing and the dustbins. Shame!)

Life is quieter now, but I have more time for the family and the home. And the more you go slowly, you can appreciate the things which make you happiest. Our busy modern life stops us thinking and appreciating.

I'm walking around inside without a stick with the aid of a foot orthotic and climbing the stairs with a handrail. I still walk outside with a stick because the uneven surfaces and unexpected situations challenge me.

My language is coming along, but it's disjointed and incoherent, especially when I'm under pressure with a person waiting for an answer. Many words "disappear" into a black void and I can't fetch them back. It's frustrating. Also my numbers and alphabet are coming back, but I struggle to estimate the the time and calculate timing to plan the day. It's so frustrating.

The complexity of the English language never surprises me and I'm always questioning the oddities of the English language. But I make it worse – together with losing the words I want, I substitute incorrect or made-up ones; with jumbling up the order, an incoherent sentence results.

Sometimes, I blurt out the phrase found first. There are many situations I say the quite the opposite word, for example, Good Evening instead of Good Morning, Goodbye instead of Hello. I laugh at myself to cover people's embarrassment and confusion.

Linked to communication, appropriate behaviour is key. I needed to relearn appropriate greetings too – one time I hugged the podiatrist to thank him and declared love to my postman – the former ended up speedily giving me the tape with an alarmed look, advising me do it at home instead. The latter ended up much happier – he responded with a raucous laugh and said I'd made his day!

Now I realise communication is the key to life. Especially dependent people, needing to ask favours and explain instructions. I got frustrated when I couldn't tell others my needs and wants. I was imprisoned in my body, taken hostage by my lack of communication.

My left arm will not come back because of the high "tone", but I'm used to living life one-handed now. I use my initiative when I cook, carry or am tasking. I'm lucky to have long and dexterous fingers!

Many things are tricky for me – can you take a photo with your mobile one-handed? And put items in a bag? Open a jar? Sew name tapes on? Hang clothes on a hanger? Tie a knot? Open a packet? In a few of these instances, I use my teeth or other parts of the body to substitute my left hand. It's slow and tedious, but I feel deep satisfaction when the task is completed.

Chapter Three
How to Understand People with Dementia

It's Confusion

Insight

Think about being woken in the middle of the night – your brain is confused as it was resting, not alert and working. You ask yourself many questions to understand the situation. Where am I? Why did I wake up? Is this a dream?

I feel like this in unfamiliar situations. I can't think quickly to work out the "clues" of the moment. The people, setting, and conversation all contribute to the understanding of it.

Why?

The short-term memory goes first. If you don't have any short-term memory, these "clues" such as the surroundings and the company, you don't understand the current situation. It results in confusion.

Have you thought to yourself while standing in a room, "Why am I here?" (For the over 50s only!) You can't remember your task – you need to retrace your steps to find the thought again.

Dementia sufferers are always in this confused state.

Imagine a giant tree with strong roots and trunk with flitting birds trying to land on it in high winds. The short-term memories are these birds. A few land successfully, some are wobbly on the small branches and most of them can't stay – they fly away immediately.

Action!

- The outside world is bewildering – when you are with the dementia sufferer, stay inside their home as much time as possible.
- Make their home an easy and calm environment (see Chapter Four).
- Don't ask too many questions. It's hard to decide through the fog of confusion.
- If you need to ask a question, it needs to be closed, i.e. they have to only answer "yes" or "no". It's then a simple decision.
- Greet the sufferer with a simple, straightforward greeting, for example, "Good Morning" or "Hello". The popular current greetings "How are you?" and "All right?" confuse them because the question demands an answer if the greeter wants it or doesn't! At the start, I answered with details of every medical condition to the bemused greeter as it was the correct answer. Quite literally.

It's Denial

Insight

Immediately when I returned home, three months after the vasospasm, I wanted to return to work. I thought my life would return to normal. My previous employer, a local public school, listened to me and made time to investigate the possibilities, but it never happened. Looking back on it, I clearly wasn't ready for it, physically and mentally.

Why?

Dementia slowly gets a hold on a person. Like ivy strangling a tree.

They can't accept and acknowledge the slow and steady disappearing pieces of the life jigsaw.

Also, people with brain damage can't think objectively about their situation. They can't see their unfamiliar actions and words might be odd. They don't want to hear the medical advice and can't remember the useful hints from helpful people.

Thus, they think themselves "suffering only from old age" or "Forgetfulness is a sign of old age." Sadly, it's more severe than that.

If you feel a parent's personality is changing or the aging process is quickly taking over, seek advice. GPs have a general test for dementia. If they discover dementia, start planning to create a safe and calm home for them (see Chapter Four).

It's Obsession

Insight

Before the disaster, I never tidied the shelves – but now I'm obsessively making rows of jars, tins, bottles, and biscuit packets, with the label outwards. Once I made labels for the shelves of the food and cooking equipment cupboards to instruct the family! They ignored them. I began on the wardrobes instead.

Why?

I needed patterns and routines to contain my chaotic thinking and walking. I couldn't control my words and my limbs, but I could control my deeds.

Action!

- Be patient
- Be understanding
- Ignore their obsessive behaviour

It's Frustration

Insight

I took it out on those people nearest to me – my husband, parents, and sister. They couldn't walk away. And old resentments I didn't know I had, came out. My personality changed for the worse and luckily my husband and parents took it with dignity and understanding.

How?

People want to be independent and successful at whatever they do. If you can't do things as before, it's frustrating and upsetting.

Action!

- Involve them in simple and unimportant tasks, set up to be successful, for example, watering the house plants, plump the cushions up or rake the leaves up in the garden. Choose a task which they enjoyed in the past.
- Support their successes and failings with understanding and no fuss.

It's Fatigue (medical term for chronic tiredness)

Insight

Fatigue is my invisible conquering enemy. It isn't just ordinary "tiredness". It's like your brain shutting down. I can't think, speak or balance.

Why?

My brain has to work very hard because it needs to work all the time to acquire new skills, as well as previous automated functions like balance, walking and talking.

That's why we like our routines – you don't have to think about them and automatically do them. My fatigue is lessening as I have my routines now at home.

However, my brain has to work constantly, especially multitasking when I need to speak. For example, making a pot of tea, which I don't do often, is a simple act for a healthy brain. It's an enormous trial to me because the task isn't automatic in my subconscious.

- First decide to use a teapot or not?
- Where's the kettle?
- Fill it up with water
- What way is the tap's on?
- Where are the teabags?
- How many?
- Where are the mugs?
- What mug size?
- How many mugs?
- What do I say about the milk and sugar?
- Where's the milk and sugar?
- Do I need a teaspoon?
- Listen to the answers
- Remember them
- Work out filling mugs with the desired quantities
- Include my choice
- Ask them: do you want biscuits with the tea?
- Ask them to sit down
- Have I enough chairs?

- Count the chairs (not easy)
- Can I carry a tray with a full teapot and so many mugs?

My brain is working hard sequencing this simple task. And having to stand up and balance. Especially when the guests want to talk to me.

It's exhausting.

A damaged brain needs to work hard because it's learning all the time. Like a rowing boat racing with a yacht in full wind. You need to work hard rowing to keep up.

Especially in the instance of every short-term memory getting lost.

Action!

- Calculate time for them to have sleeps and rests throughout the day.
- Invest in an electric reclining chair which turns into "bed" with one press of a button; it's important for downstairs naps.
- Don't ask too many questions
- Do follow a routine
- Quieten and calm down (see Chapter Four)

It's Despair and Fear

Insight

I remember the first night in the hospital, surrounded by strangers, not knowing what was going on. I felt frightened for the first time in my adult life. I felt desperate, alone, vulnerable, and scared.

Why?

Dementia sufferers have this feeling all the time as their short-term memories have gone. They can't remember the room and people surrounding them all the time.

Adults are in control for all of their lives and it's frightening when you can't understand the situation and can't control your mind and body – hence your life.

Action!

- Make them feel safe and loved.
- Repeat your name and relationship time and again.
- Don't be frustrated with them.

Chapter Four
How to Care for People with Dementia

Create a calm home

- Designate one major carer who manages the others to avoid confusion.
- Put on their favourite music instead of television. (TV emits confusing and distracting voices.) Or if trying to decide what choice is hard, then Classic FM (FM 99.9-101.9 HMz) is my choice of background radio station. It has frequent news headlines if you want them and I ignore the annoying ads!
- Deter cold callers with signs: "No Cold Callers". The signs aren't rude; they are rude disturbing people in their homes and sanctuaries.
- Programme their computer with a spam folder for nuisance emails.
- Concentrating the mind is calming. Buy those mindfulness colouring books or puzzles.

Create a safe home

- Remove any trip hazards, for example, rugs, electrical wires.
- Highlight any uneven room entrances with duct tape.
- Light up dark corridors with battery-driven motion- sensor lights stuck on the skirting boards.
- Check the fire alarms weekly.
- Check the door locks are working and the spare keys are in a known place.
- On windy days, make sure the outside doors are wedged open to prohibit crushed fingers. (I always place my hand on the doorway surround to steady myself.)
- Install grab rails beside steps if needed.

Set A Routine

- Set a schedule for each week. For example, visit on a set time or day.
- Plan each meal for a set time in the day.
- Make sure their nap times, bedtimes, and wake-up times are regular.
- Purchase a desk diary and use it for communicating with other carers by writing notes in the appropriate day.
- Plan ahead and give clear instructions
- Take time to explain everything – the tasks one step at a time.
- Don't confuse the sufferer by contradictions.
- Write all instructions down to remind them. I go through copious post-it notes!

Slow Down

- They only need peace and quiet, they don't need ventures out to stave off boredom and have fresh air, like you. They want to just exist and understand what's going on.
- One outing per day is fine.
- A few visitors per day is enough.
- Try not to rush about.
- Go at their pace. You will think it's very slow, but confusion needs time to sort out.

Don't Hurry

- Don't hurry the sufferer. Confusion needs time. An easy task for you isn't easy for them. For example, you inform them, "We are going out at two." You are in control and know the sequence of events – check the time now, calculate the time to go, get on your coat, check for money and keys. Easy. But poses many questions for the sufferer:
- Two in the morning or afternoon?
- And when is two o'clock? (needs to understand time).
- How much time do I have? (needs to calculate time).
- Where is the door?
- Do I get on my coat and shoes?
- What other items do I need?
- Why are we going out?

Hence dithering and inactivity.

It's better to tell them with lots of time and with lots of information, for example: "At two in the afternoon, after lunch, we are going out to the doctors for your flu jab. We need coats because it's cold. I will warn you one hour before we need to leave."

And leave a note to remind them.

Quieten Down

- They don't need constant chats – they need quiet.
- Resist talking constantly at them to ease your discomfort of silences or, even worse, never hum or sing to fill the silences. It's a nightmare for their overloaded brains.
- Talk with them, not at them. Wait for their answers.
- Stay indoors by choice. Outside the home is challenging. Noisy and busy surroundings need many senses to work. I remember the first time I visited a supermarket. A huge wave of loud noise engulfed me like a tsunami, and I stopped still to take in the loud cacophony. Even now, I stop walking on the pavement to concentrate to understand a loud noise near me, like a speeding motorbike or a loud mobile chat.

Connect with Long-term Memories

- If their long-term memories are still intact, use these long-term memories to communicate with them. Unlock your previous relationship by using a Memory Box, full of their favourite objects from your childhood, including presents you gave them and vice versa.
- If their long-term memory has gone, you need to build a new relationship. Do reintroduce yourself each time, describing your relationship to the sufferer. For example, "I'm Jane, your eldest daughter."
- Don't take it personally if they can't recognise you.
- Don't condescend. They are struggling adults, not children.
- Don't be angry. They are not acting difficult on purpose, like a teenager. It's memory loss.

Restore Their Dignity

- They were once independent adults and dependence is undignified. Restoring dignity is easy – having purpose in life.
- Teach them to do simple or unimportant tasks depending on their skill set. For example, sweep the kitchen floor, wipe the table or draw the curtains.
- Make sure any other health issues are not being ignored and organise their appointments with the opticians, dentist and audiologists.
- A visit to their hairdresser/barber's will boost morale.

N.B. Warn these people beforehand to treat the sufferer with understanding.

Break the Communication Barrier

I understand now how communication is vital.

- If the sufferer is struggling with speech, try hand signals or writing notes instead.
- If you can't communicate, physical contact is vital. Give lots of hugs, rest your hand on their shoulder, link arms or hold hands when you walk. They may look frail, but they won't break!

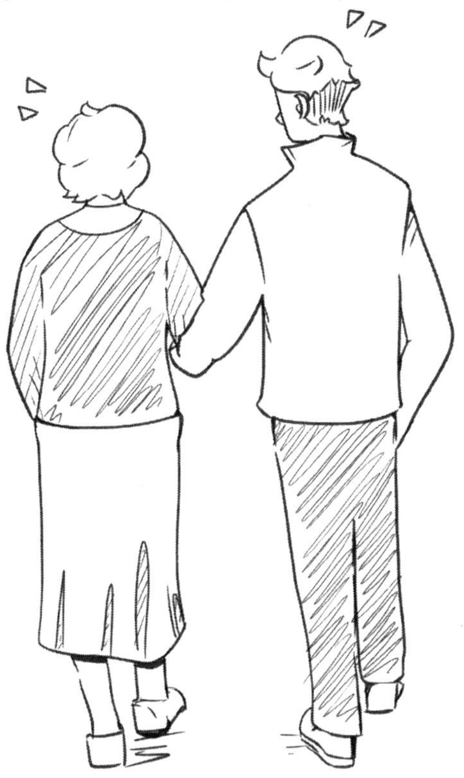